A catalogue record for this book is available from the British Library

Published by Ladybird Books Ltd
80 Strand London WC2R 0RL
A Penguin Company

2 4 6 8 10 9 7 5 3 1

LADYBIRD and the device of a ladybird are
trademarks of Ladybird Books Ltd
© Walt Disney Enterprises 2002

Printed in China

DISNEY's

RETURN TO
NEVER · LAND

Ladybird

Once, long ago, a young girl called Wendy waved goodbye to her magical friend, Peter Pan, as he flew back home to Never Land.

Years passed, and a grown-up Wendy
found herself waving goodbye again – this
time to her husband, Edward. He was off
to fight in the war.

While the war dragged on, Wendy kept
her son, Danny, happy with tales of Peter
Pan. But her daughter, Jane, thought such
stories were childish. Jane's father had
asked her to take care of the family while
he was away so she had to act grown-up.

One night, Jane was out with Nana-Two, their dog, when an air raid began.

Jane rushed home to join her mother and Danny in their air raid shelter. Danny was scared, but Wendy said the noises were the cannons on Captain Hook's pirate ship.

She told Danny how Peter Pan had captured Hook's treasure. Then Peter's fairy friend, Tinker Bell, had used pixie dust to make the ship float away.

"Hook will never win," said Wendy, finishing her story, "as long as there is faith, trust and pixie dust."

"Poppycock!" said Jane, who was writing a list of supplies in her notebook.

Later that evening, a warden called at the house to tell Wendy that Danny and Jane were going to be evacuated. They were to be taken away to the country, where they would be safe from air raids.

Wendy asked Jane to look after Danny while they were away, and tell him Peter Pan stories. "We'll be together again," promised Wendy. "You must have faith."

"Faith, trust, pixie dust. Mother, those are just words from your story!" cried Jane, upset and angry. "Daniel, grow up! It's just a lot of childish nonsense!"

"You're lying!" yelled Danny, and he ran out of the room.

Jane felt very guilty about upsetting Danny, and cried herself to sleep.

In the night, a noise woke her. It was Captain Hook and his pirates. They threw Jane into a sack! "I've got a surprise for you, Peter Pan," Hook said to himself.

When they arrived in Never Land, Hook
tried to use Jane as bait to trap Peter Pan.
But Peter avoided both Hook and a
hungry octopus to rescue the sack. He
was very surprised to find
Jane inside – he had
thought he was rescuing
his old friend, Wendy!
And Jane couldn't
believe it – Peter Pan
was real!

Peter took Jane to his treehouse home to meet the Lost Boys.

He told them that Jane was their new mother – just as Wendy had once been.

The boys wanted Jane to tell them a story, but Jane said she wasn't very good at stories, so Peter suggested a treasure hunt.

"C'mon, Jane, let's go find the treasure," yelled the boys.

"No," Jane said sadly. "I must go home."

Jane missed her family and wanted to tell them she was sorry.

The Lost Boys, disappointed, didn't understand why Jane wanted to leave. "What's the matter with her?" they asked.

"I don't know," said Peter, puzzled. "She acts kinda like a…grown-up."

Later, Peter found Jane building a raft to sail home on. He and Tinker Bell watched as Jane climbed aboard – and sank.

Peter lifted her from the water. "The only way out of here is to fly," he told her. He took Jane back to the woods, to meet up with the Lost Boys once again.

Tinker Bell sprinkled magic dust on the Lost Boys, and they began to fly!

"Look, anybody can do it!" they cried. "All it takes is faith, trust…"

"And pixie dust?" said Jane, unimpressed.

But even with a good sprinkling of Tinker Bell's special dust, Jane still couldn't fly.

She felt cross and unhappy – especially when the Lost Boys teased her. She would never get home! "I don't believe in any of this – and I especially don't believe in fairies!" she shouted, and stomped off.

Just then, Tinker Bell fell to the ground, her light fading.

The boys gathered round Tinker Bell.
"If we don't get Jane to believe in fairies,
Tink's light is going to go out!" said Peter.
"We've got to make her one of us."
He knew this would help Jane believe.
They set off to look for her.

But Captain Hook found Jane first. He promised to take her home on his pirate ship, if she helped him to get his treasure back from Peter. Jane agreed as long as Captain Hook promised not to hurt Peter.

"When you find the treasure, blow this," said Hook slyly, handing Jane a whistle.

At last, Peter and the Lost Boys caught up with Jane. They showed her how to have fun like a Lost Boy. She loved it!

Then, riding on a log with Peter, she surged into Dead Man's Cave. And there was the famous treasure – lots and lots of jewels! Jane thought of whistling for Hook, but changed her mind. These were her friends and she was the first Lost Girl ever!

But soon the fun ended. One of the Lost Boys found Captain Hook's whistle – and blew it!

Hook and his pirates swooped into the cave and rounded up Peter and his gang. Peter thought Jane had betrayed them. "You lied to me!" he said. "And because you don't believe in fairies, Tink's light is going out." Jane was upset. Peter and his friends were in trouble, and it was her fault

Hook took his prisoners to the ship, and Jane ran off to look for Tinker Bell.

When she found her, the little fairy's light had almost faded to nothing.

"Oh, Tinker Bell, I'm so sorry!" sobbed Jane and, as she spoke, Jane really did begin to believe in fairies.

And slowly, magically, the tiny fairy's light began to brighten. Before long, Tink was her old sparkling self again.

Jane quickly thought of Peter and raced, with Tinker Bell, to the *Jolly Roger*.

She freed the Lost Boys, then stole the key to Peter's padlock from Hook. The angry captain chased her up the mast.

Jane faced him bravely. "Don't you see, Hook, you'll never win, as long as there's faith, trust…and pixie dust!" she said.

Tinker Bell did her stuff, sprinkling Jane with magic dust, and Jane flew at last – straight down to unlock Peter.

Soon Captain Hook was fleeing for his life, chased by the still-hungry octopus.

The fight was over, the pirates were gone, and the friends were safe. Before long, Peter and Tinker Bell were flying with Jane, back to her home in London.

Wendy loved seeing Peter Pan and Tinker Bell again. Jane was soon telling her and Danny – and of course Nana-Two – every single detail of the adventure.

As Peter left, Jane promised softly, "I'll always believe in you, Peter Pan."

Peter and Tinker Bell hovered in the night sky for a moment. They watched as a truck pulled up outside Jane's house. A man got out, and they heard Jane cry out happily, "Daddy's back!"

Peter smiled. "Let's go home, Tink."